KU-198-321

Folk Tales

Compiled by Wu Min

CHINA INTERCONTINENTAL PRESS

图书在版编目（CIP）数据

中国民间故事:英文/伍民编;李意祺,汉定译.-北京:
五洲传播出版社，2011.1（2012.6重印）
（中国经典故事系列）
ISBN 978-7-5085-1772-8
Ⅰ.①中… Ⅱ.①伍… ②李… ③汉… Ⅲ.①民间
故事-作品集-中国-英文 Ⅳ.①I277.3
中国版本图书馆CIP数据核字(2012)第112694号

出 版 人：荆孝敏
编　　者：伍　民
翻　　译：李意祺　汉　定
责任编辑：王　莉
设计指导：缪　惟
设计制作：苑立静
插　　图：台双垣　李思东

中国民间故事

出版发行：五洲传播出版社
社　　址：北京市海淀区莲花池东路北小马厂6号
邮政编码：100038
发行电话：010-82001447
制版单位：北京锦绣圣艺文化发展有限公司
印　　刷：北京圣彩虹制版印刷技术有限公司
开　　本：787x1092　1/32
印　　张：5.25
版　　次：2011年1月第1版　2012年6月第2次印刷
书　　号：ISBN 978-7-5085-1772-8
定　　价：53.00元

Preface

When the apes finally evolved into Man, they awoke to find a world they enjoyed and innumerable things which were beyond their imagination. Wow! Why? Fantastic folk tales were thus created.

Such tales were passed down through history orally, but are still told today. The more recent versions are, of course, masterpieces of modern fiction.

This book is highlighted with the inclusion of the Four Most-Favored Folk Love

Tales of China.

Liang Shanbo and Zhu Yingtai (or *The Butterfly Lovers*). It is a Chinese legend about the tragic romance between two lovers, Liang Shanbo and Zhu Yingtai, who died for love and became reincarnated as two butterflies flying freely together. The legend is often regarded as the Chinese equivalent of *Romeo and Juliet*.

Legend of the White Snake. It is an ancient Chinese story in which a snake lady one day happened to meet a scholar and they fell in love and got married. They enjoyed their life, but unfortunately suffered from the evil ministrations of a sorcerer-monk.

Great Wall Collapse as Meng Jiang Nu Cried. Meng Jiang Nu is said to have trudged a great distance to the Great Wall with the purpose of bringing winter clothes for her husband, a Wall builder. On learning that he was dead and buried under the Great Wall,

she cried so loudly that a large section of the Great Wall collapsed over her.

The Cowherd and the Weaver Maid (or *Niu Lang and Zhi Nu*). This tells of the source of the Chinese equivalent of Valentine's Day, which is comparably romantic yet heartrending, because this is the only time of year when the Cowherd and the Weaver Maid meet each other across the Milky Way.

In China, operas, plays, music and movies, based on the theme of folk tales, are very popular. From these, our readers, especially those are still young, will gain a love and understanding of traditional Chinese culture.

CONTENTS

Legend of the White Snake

A cave in the Emei Mountain of Sichuan Province was home to Master Lishan Laomu. The master had two disciples, both snake demons - the female white snake who had been cultivating herself under the Master for some 1,000 years and the female green snake who has been doing the same for about 800 years. The two snake demons had hearts of gold and never attacked human people.

One fine day, the two snake demons, who felt lonely in the meditation cave, incarnated themselves into two beautiful girls:

Bai Suzhen and Xiao Qing, Bai meaning white and Qing green. They descended to Hangzhou, hailed as the "Paradise on Earth".

They were enjoying the smiling lotuses on the West Lake by the Broken Bridge when dark clouds gathered and thunder began rumbling in the sky. A downpour was obviously imminent.

Bai and Qing both possessed the magic power to turn something by the road into the umbrellas they needed, but how could they do so when there were so many people around?

What was to be done then? A young man came over and addressed them politely, "Don't worry. You may use my umbrella."

Bai and Qing accepted the offer and promised to return it the next day.

The next day saw the two snake ladies go and visit the young man at the given address. They found he was Xu Xian and his parents were dead. He lived with his sister's family and worked in a drug store.

As Xu was handsome and honest, Bai

fell in love with him and, with the assistance of Qing, they were married.

The young couple moved out of Xu's sister's home and opened a drugstore by a picturesque lake lined with blossoming peach flowers and weeping willows. Xu was good with the customers and Bai, his wife, boasted the magic power to find needed herbal remedies. The business boomed and the two lived happily along with Qing.

One day a monk seeking alms came and told Xu he was Abbot Fahai from the Jinshan Temple in Zhengjiang.

"You carry an inhuman outlook in your face," the monk said. "There must be a demon haunting your family."

"Wrong!" replied Xu, who went on to tell the monk there were only his wife and servant Qing at home.

The monk said: "Your wife is the said demon. Keep this knowledge secret and wait for the Festival that falls on the fifth day of the fifth lunar month. By then you should

have tried your best to make her drink a cup of Realgar Wine. If you can do so, everything will become clear. You are more than welcome to visit me if you come across any problems."

When the wife Bai drank a cup of Realgar Wine that day, she felt dizzy and hurried to ask Qing to support her back to her bed chamber.

Worried about her health, the husband Xu went to examine what had happened to her. As he lifted up the mosquito net, a giant white snake, thick as a water bucket, was found sleeping in the bed and there was the smell of alcohol on its breath.

Xu cried out and was terrified out of his wits. Then he fainted and fell to the floor. Woken up by Xu's terrifying cry, the white snake transformed itself into Xu's lovely wife Bai.

Bai and her sister Qing carried Xu onto the bed but the man's eyes remained closed and his soul had obviously left his body.

"He won't come back until he is fed with Glossy Ganoderma," the wife Bai said.

"Where can we find it?" Qing replied.

"Lingshan Mountain. But the immortals there refuse anyone who goes in search of the elixir."

After a moment's thought, Qing told Bai she would go. "You should stay at home because you are carrying a child," Qing said.

"Thank you. But my husband is in imminent danger, so I have to go myself."

Bai rode on drifting clouds toward the Lingshan Mountain.

A deer spirit and a crane spirit were on duty that day. They fought with Bai, forcing her to retreat step by step. Bai, who was pregnant, was exhausted and her life hung in the balance. But for the sake of the life of her husband Xu, Bai frenetically went on fighting the two deity guards, her hair drooping loosely over her shoulders and her face reddened as a result of the desperate struggle.

"Stop!" shouted the master god of the

mountain, Star of Long Life, who appeared above them.

Bai bowed to the immortal, seeking forgiveness for her coming to steal Glossy Ganoderma which, she asserted, was the only thing that could save the life of her husband.

"You yearn for living on earth and are destined to suffer," sighed Star of Long Life, who then ordered his guards to stop fighting Bai and let her go and pick a Glossy Ganoderma.

Bai bowed three times again to the revered deity master and left like the wind.

Having been fed with Glossy Ganoderma, Xu Xian opened his eyes slowly, and his wife Bai Suzhen breathed a great sigh of relief.

"Are.... You're...." Xu Xian appeared astonished when he saw his wife Bai.

Bai consoled her husband by saying she had killed the white snake.

"If you do not believe me, get up and I will show you the dead snake."

Xu got out of the bed, and went with his wife to the courtyard where he found a dead snake, thick as a water bucket.

Despite this evidence, Xu still doubted the truth of what his wife told him.

One day, he found an excuse for visiting the Jinshan Temple in Zhengjiang so as to meet Abbot Fahai.

"You carry an even heavier devilish appearance than when compared to the previous time," Abbot Fahai said.

"But I found nothing wrong with my wife," replied Xu Xian.

"Well, that's because she has been cultivating herself for some 1,000 years," said Abbot Fahai. "But, don't worry. In no more than one month I will overcome her and put her under the pagoda for ever so that she will no longer cause damage to you or others in the future."

Xu refused to believe what the abbot had said as he loved his wife very much and could not forget how good she was to him.

"Thank you very much, Abbot Fahai. But no matter what you say to me, I can not believe my lovely wife is a demon. Please keep your hands off matters concerning my wife and I," Xu said.

Xu was about to leave when Master Fahai ordered his disciples to block his way.

"You must not leave, otherwise you will be bogged down deeper in the mire," said Abbot Fahai, refusing to let him go.

After her husband had not returned for several days, Bai was on tenterhooks day and night. Finally she and Qing went over to the Jinshan Temple in Zhengjiang.

Abbot Fahai, holding a Buddhist bowl in his hand, blocked their way.

"Stop! You have the effrontery to come here? You may have taken the road to Paradise but instead you choose to take the way to Hell," Master Fahai said.

Qing, her eyes blazing with anger, shouted at the monk,"You - Bald Monk, release my brother-in-law and you will have

peace. Otherwise, you will know more trouble than you can conceive of and your temple will be destroyed along with you."

Flying into a rage, Abbot Fahai jumped toward Qing, his red kasaya fluttering in the wind. He wielded a Buddhist monk's staff, which is extremely heavy, and threw himself into a fierce fight with Qing.

As Bai was pregnant, she could not confront the abbot herself, but instead she pulled a golden hairpin from her head and waved it in the breeze. Immediately, a ferociously surging river rushed to surround the temple, and an army of shrimp and crab soldiers rose out of the waters, their weapons clashing to produce a terrifying sound.

Astonished to see this, Abbot Fahai grabbed his kasaya and threw it into the air. The kasaya expanded to cover the temple, protecting it from invasion by water and river-borne invaders. With the protection of the kasaya, the temple rose with the rising of the water. Hours later, Bai had to admit defeat and

returned the river to Hangzhou.

Seeing that his wife Bai possessed the magic power to make a river attack the Jinshan Temple, Xu came to realize his wife was not human. With this understanding, his mind rested at ease. Recalling her kindness and loveliness he found nothing terrifying in having the white snake demon as his wife.

One day, catching Abbot Fahai unawares, Xu managed to leave the Jinshan Temple. He hurried back to Hangzhou.

Neither Bai nor Qing were at home.

When Xu rushed to the Broken Bridge by the West Lake, where he had met them for the first time, he found both of them sitting in a boat.

Qing was angered to see him, "You have the face to come and see us? Why don't you bring the bald monk to suppress us also?"

Bai appeared disappointed when she first saw him: "Dear husband, we have been together for some time and you should know what I am and whether I am good to you or not."

Tears rolled down her cheeks.

Xu was very upset and said with great honesty, "Dear wife, I have made a mistake. I am sorry for this."

Peace returned and the three went back home merrily.

A few months later, Bai gave birth to a lovely son and Xu smiled from ear to ear. On the 31st day after the baby's birth, a month-old party was held but, unexpectedly, Abbot Fahai came with a Buddhist alms bowl in his hand.

Xu stepped in front of the door and blocked the Abbot's entrance.

"Stop, please. I know what my wife is. And yet I love her from the bottom of my heart. Please don't interfere," said Xu to Abbot Fahai.

"Amitabha! Dear Benefactor," said the Abbot, "no matter what you say, it is a fact that she is a snake spirit. She will do you no good in the end. I come for your safety."

Before he had even finished speaking these words, he slipped past Xu and went directly into the room where Bai was resting.

Having so recently given birth to her son she was powerless against him.

The Abbot held the Buddhist monk's bowl high in the air, producing an all-powerful force directed straight at Bai.

Qing instantly rushed forward, but was stopped by Bai who was about to be sucked into the Buddhist alms bowl. Bai shouted to Qing, "He dares not kill me! You Go! Work hard at developing your own magic power and then come back and fight him."

Bai was drawn into the alms bowl which Abbot Fahai subsequently buried underneath the Leifeng Pagoda towering over the West Lake in Hangzhou. And he himself remained in the Jingci Temple not far from the pagoda.

Qing fled to the Emei Mountain where she worked with might and main for 18 years. Armed to the teeth in terms of the magic power she had mastered, Qing went to take

revenge on Abbot Fahai.

Abbot Fahai was 18 years older when he fought Qing that day. After fighting for a while, he felt tired and found it hard to maintain the struggle.

Qing waved her sword at the Leifeng Pagoda.

The pagoda collapsed with a big crash! Out of it dashed Bai towards Abbot Fahai who had been responsible for her 18 years of imprisonment in the pagoda.

Abbot Fahai was forced to retreat into the West Lake, hiding himself behind the shell of a crab.

Bai and Qing rushed back home, there finding Xu with grey hair and a young man who was tall and strong. They lived a happy life thereafter, free from any interference.

The Story of Mr. Dongguo and the Zhongshan Wolf

The Story of the Fisherman and the Monster in *1001 Arabian Nights* is popular all over the world. Actually China has a story that is very similar to it. This version of a well-known story is called "Mr. Dongguo and the Zhongshan Wolf."

The story comes from the *Biography of Dongtian* written by Ma Zhongxi in the Ming Dynasty (1644-1911) of China. As the story goes, there was a pedantic scholar named Mr. Dongguo who was a bookworm but who read books in a mechanical way. One day, he mounted his donkey, loaded it with a bag of books and rode to a place named "Zhongshan State" to seek an official position. All of a sudden, an injured wolf jumped out in front of him and humbly and pitifully addressed him thus,"Sir, I am fleeing from a hunter who has wounded me with one of his arrows. I was nearly killed. Please help me and hide me in your bag and I will repay your kindness later." Mr. Dongguo certainly knew that wolves often harm people, but he felt sorry for this particular wolf. He had a think and then said, "If I help you, I would offend the hunter. But now that you have begged me, I will surely find some way to save you." Mr. Dongguo had the wolf curl itself into a ball, tied it with a length of rope, and made its body small enough to be put into the bag which was used to hold the books.

A moment later the hunter appeared. He asked Mr. Dongguo, "Sir, have you seen a wolf? Where did it run?" Mr. Dongguo replied, "I have not seen any wolf. There are

many roads that fork off this road. Maybe it fled down one of those." The hunter believed Mr. Dongguo's words, and immediately headed off in another direction. After hearing the hunter's horse fade into the distance, the wolf addressed Mr. Dongguo, saying, "Sir, please let me out and I can make my own escape." Mr. Dongguo, being of a merciful disposition, could not resist its sweet words and let it out. Unexpectedly the wolf howled, "If you help somebody once, you should help him completely. Now I'm hungry. Help me again and let me eat you!" And as he said this, he pounced on Mr. Dongguo.

As Mr. Dongguo was bare-handedly struggling with the wolf, he shouted to it, "You are an ungrateful wretch!" Just at that moment, an old peasant with a hoe over his shoulder came up. Mr. Dongguo grabbed the peasant's arm and told him how he had saved the wolf and how the wolf wanted to eat him in return for his kindness. But the wolf wouldn't admit that Mr. Dongguo had saved

his life. The peasant thought for a moment and then said, "I don't believe you. How could such a big wolf fit in a bag that size? I won't believe it unless I see it with my own eyes." The wolf agreed. It lay on the ground, curled up, and was once again trussed up with the rope by Mr. Dongguo and put into the bag. The peasant tied up the mouth of the bag and said to Mr. Dongguo, "You cannot change the fact that it is a wolf's nature to eat people. You have been merciful to this wolf, and that was very foolish of you!" Then, he raised his hoe and beat the wolf to death.

Mr. Dongguo was suitably humbled and much appreciated the peasant's saving his life. Now, "Mr. Dongguo" and "Zhongshan Wolf" are set phrases in Chinese. "Mr. Dongguo" refers to those who cannot tell good people from bad, and who give sympathy to those who will take advantage of it. "Zhongshan Wolf" refers to ungrateful people who return good with evil.

Lotus Lantern

There are five Taoist mountains in China: Taishan Mountain (called Dongyue in Shandong Province), Hengshan Mountain (Nanyue in Hunan Province), Huashan Mountain (Xiyue in Shaanxi Province), Hengshan Mountain (Beiyue in Shanxi Province) and Songshan Mountain (Zhongyue in Henan Province).

Of these, the Huashan Mountain (Xiyue) boasts five major peaks, with the east peak facing the rising sun, the southern peak serving as home to many wild geese,

the western peak being where lotuses grow, and the middle peak known as Jadite Girl. Together they blossom like a flower, hence the alternative name Flower Mountain, "flower" being pronounced "hua" in Chinese.

The guardian of the mountain was a water-like fairy called Third Goddess (San Shengmu) of Huashan. Living in a palace standing atop the Lotus Peak, she took care of the Lotus Lantern that had been presented by the Queen Mother of the West.

The Lotus Lantern possessed magic powers. When illuminated by it, all the immortals and devils would lose their own magic powers as a result. Extremely kind-hearted, the Third Goddess often took pains to show the way to those who became lost on the mountain, or helped those in financial difficulties.

One day, it snowed heavily and the wind howled. No one came for pilgrimage. Suddenly, however, as the fairy was singing and dancing merrily in her palace hall, a man

pushed open the door and entered in a gust of wind and snow. Swiftly she regained her throne, presenting her official image as a statue of the Third Goddess of the Huashan Mountain, worshipped by all.

The man, named Liu Yanchang, simply wanted shelter from the wind and cold. He was on his way to the capital city to take part in the imperial examination but now found himself trapped on the snow-covered mountain.

As he examined the sacred statue of the Third Goddess, he was spellbound by her beauty and, after a while, sighed because unfortunately she was only a statue of a Goddess, not a real woman.

Out of his admiration for the Third Goddess, he took out his writing brush and composed a poem on the wall, reading:

Finding myself in a wonderland,

I discover a beauty lovelier than peach flowers.

Heart-broken am I, Liu Yan,

For the only place to meet her is in dreams.

The Third Goddess watched Liu all the while, feeling at a loss as to what to do. He was handsome, smart and talented but she still racked her brains to find suitable adjectives to describe him. She told herself that she had fallen in love with him just as he had shown his love for her. But, how could a fairy marry a mortal man? It was not possible.

When the snow had stopped falling and the ferocious winds no longer howled, Liu left the hall sadly. And the Third Goddess was equally reluctant to see him go, her eyes shining with tears .

The Goddess followed the young man with her eyes until he was out of sight.

Shortly after Liu Yanchang left the Temple of the Goddess, a dense fog suddenly enveloped the mountain, making it difficult to take even one step. Moreover, howls of wolves and roars of tigers came from all sides. The Goddess was worried about the scholar who traveled thus alone and promptly went out after him with her lotus lantern. Suddenly, she heard a cry for help from within the vast stretch of dense fog. A fierce tiger was attacking Liu Yanchang. The Goddess hastened to use the magic lotus lantern to illuminate the scene; the clouds and fog vanished at once and the tiger ran off. Liu Yanchang recognized that it was the Goddess who had rescued him. They looked at each other face to face and finally threw themselves into each other's arms.

They were deeply attached to each other after they got married. Subsequently, when the imperial examination date was drawing near, the Goddess was pregnant. Before Liu resumed his journey to take the examination, he presented the Goddess with a piece of Chenxiang (gharu-wood) handed down from his ancestors and said that their son should be named Chenxiang. The Goddess walked for a long distance with Liu and they were both very much loath to part.

However, the God Erlang, elder brother of the Goddess, finally received the news that his sister had secretly married with a mortal. The God Erlang was imperious and fusty. In his opinion his sister had not only violated heavenly regulations but also brought shame on the family and caused him to lose face in the heavenly palace. He was afraid of his own position if the Jade Emperor condemned his sister. Without hesitation, he dispatched heavenly generals and soldiers and sent out his heavenly dog to Huashan Mountain to confront his sister.

The result was a disagreeable conversation that led to them fighting each other. But with the protection of the lotus lantern, it was hard for God Erlang to attack the Third Goddess. After a while, however, the Third Goddess suddenly felt a pain in her belly. She staggered, and the heavenly dog took this opportunity to snatch the lotus lantern in its jaws.

Hence, God Erlang overpowered the

Third Goddess at one blow and ordered her to give up her mortal life. But the Third Goddess refused, making God Erlang extremely angry. He banished the Third Goddess into the Black Cloud Cave under the Lotus Peak, intending to keep her from ever coming out again.

The Third Goddess gave birth to her son Chenxiang in the completely dark cave. To prevent any later mishap, she wrote a letter with her own blood and concealed it within the clothes of the child. She also entrusted the God of the Land with the task of handing over the child to Liu Yanchang when he made a pilgrimage to the Temple of Goddess one month later.

Liu Yanchang succeeded in the government examination and was appointed Governor of Yangzhou. Before he took up the post, however, he especially came to Huashan Mountain. But, to his dismay, the Temple of the Goddess was full of dust and cobwebs. Though the appearance of the statue of the Goddess was as beautiful as ever, she wore an

expression of great sadness.

Suddenly, a blast of fragrant wind blew and Liu heard the cries of a child. Liu raised his head and saw a baby lying on the incense burner table. He took it in his arms at once and found a piece of gharu-wood hanging around the baby's neck and a letter written in blood in its clothes.

After reading the letter, Liu burst into tears, now understanding what had befallen the Third Goddess and that the baby was his son.

Liu took Chenxiang back to Yangzhou in tears. He employed an ayah and brought up the boy with great care. Chenxiang grew steadily day by day and became both clever and strong.

At the age of 13, Chenxiang accidently discovered the letter written by his mother and thus discovered that she was imprisoned under the Huashan Mountain. He immediately wanted to rescue his mother but his father only shook his head at the idea and sighed

deeply. One day, Chenxiang could no longer restrain himself and left without saying goodbye to his father. He went to the Huashan Mountain with the letter to rescue his mother.

He experienced innumerable trials and hardships on the journey but finally arrived at the Huashan Mountain. But, where was his mother?

He called out loudly. His miserable shouts and cries resounded in the valley, attracting the attention of an immortal named Pili Daxian who just happened to be passing. This kind immortal read the letter and felt indignant for the virtuous Third Goddess and her distressed child. After thinking for a while, he agreed to help Chenxiang rescue his mother.

Chenxiang urged the immortal to set out straight away. The immortal walked as if flying ahead and Chenxiang followed closely behind.

On the way, they came upon a great river. The immortal flew over it. However, there

was neither bridge nor ferryman. Without hesitation, Chenxiang jumped into the swiftly flowing waters, with a view to swimming across the river in order to keep up with the immortal. Fortunately, this was a heavenly river. Washed by its waters, Chenxiang was changed completely and thoroughly and endowed with supernatural strength.

The immortal also told him that a magic axe was buried in the mountain ahead which could split the Huashan Mountain. Chenxiang ran swiftly forward but encountered a raging fire. To fetch the axe, Chenxiang dived into the flames. Luckily, there was no fire inside. He saw the axe on the cliff, shining with a strange glow. Chenxiang strode one step forward and twisted off the chains that bound the axe.

Now possessing immortal power and the magic axe, Chenxiang thanked the immortal and proceeded to Huashan Mountain to rescue his mother. He found the Black Cloud Cave and called out to his mother from in front of

it. The sound penetrated layer upon layer of rocks and reached the Third Goddess

Knowing her son had come to rescue her, the Third Goddess was immensely excited. However, she knew that God Erlang was infinitely resourceful. Even Sun Wukong, who made havoc in the heavens, had been beaten by him. Chenxiang was still only a boy and God Erlang had the lotus lantern, so the former was no match for the latter. Hence, the Third Goddess asked her son not to act rashly and instead go in supplication to her brother.

Chenxiang arrived at the temple of God Erlang and tried every means to entreat him. However, God Erlang was as hard as the netherworld's millstone, and was not only unwilling to set free the Third Goddess but also lifted his broadsword with three points and two blades to aim a blow at Chenxiang.

Chenxiang was now furiously angry and brandished the axe while moving towards God Erlang. The two fought from heaven to earth, shaking the ground and overturning the

rivers and seas.

The scenes startled the Great White Planet in the heavens, who sent four fairies to have a look. After watching for a while from their seats on the clouds, the four fairies also came to believe that God Erlang was too heartless to his nephew. Hence, after giving each other a nod and a glance, they aided Chenxiang with some secret magic power. Chenxiang became increasingly valiant in the fight and God Erlang could ward off his blows no longer, barely escaping with a bad wound. The Lotus Lantern was restored to Chenxiang.

Chenxiang immediately hurried back to Huashan Mountain and came to the Black Cloud Cave. He brandished his axe and brought it down on the rock. With an earth-shaking noise, the Huashan Mountain split in two and the Goddess who had suffered captivity for 13 years saw the light of day once more, and embraced her son for a long time.

Wolf ! Wolf !

Once upon a time, a shepherd boy grazed a flock of sheep on the mountain slopes. One day, this boy called out all of a sudden, "Wolf! Wolf!"

On hearing his cries, the villagers who were going about their daily tasks of farming or chopping wood immediately laid aside their work and hurried to come to his rescue, carrying reaping-hooks, hoes and bamboo poles in their hands. However, when they arrived they found the sheep grazing docilely and no sign of any danger. "Where is the

wolf?" they asked the boy. He simply threw back his head and laughed.

There was, of course, no actual wolf but a boy who was teasing the villagers. They all got very angry and criticized him for lying. They asked him not to tell lies again and went back to their work.

A few days later, the villagers were busy with their work when again they heard the shepherd boy crying out, "Wolf! Wolf!"

Just like the last time, they laid aside their work at once and ran up to save him, reaping-hooks, hoes and bamboo poles in hand. And once more they found themselves fooled. There was not a wolf at all and the boy was again standing there laughing at them.

"We criticized you and asked you not to tell us lies again," the villagers said, "so why did you disobey us?" They boy just laughed even louder. He regarded himself as being a very superior sort of boy. Even the adults were fooled by him.

A few days later, the boy called out

again, "Wolf! Wolf! Come on! Come on! Come quickly! Wolf!"

Upon hearing his cries, no one stopped their work. One villager said, "The boy has lied to us twice, and it is certain that he is lying again this time." Another said, "We had been fooled by this boy quite enough. Not again. "

But this time there really was a wolf. It had a big red mouth wide open and very sharp teeth and it ate up all the sheep. Then it turned to eat the boy.

"Wolf! Wolf! Come on! Wolf!" shouted the boy, as he tried to run away. However, no one come to his rescue.

The boy was fortunate to roll down the hillside and redeem his own life from the jaws of the wolf, but all his sheep were eaten up. From then on, the boy dared not lie again.

The Eight Immortals Cross the Sea

Spring is just around the corner on the third day of the third lunar month, and people gather to watch the joss sticks burning in the Peach Palace. Legend has it that the birthday of the Xiwangmu (Queen Mother of the West) is celebrated on the third day of the third lunar month each year and that all the gods and immortals come to her palace, the Peach Palace, to offer their congratulations.

On that very day this year, the Peach Palace is filled with propitious clouds and immortal music. The immortals come in

succession, flying down from the cloudy regions. The Xiwangmu hastens to order her fairies to show the immortal guests to their seats. She prepares the peach feast and entertains them with the sacred peaches and celestial wine.

At this year's Peach Feast there are eight immortals newly going up to the heaven who catch the eyes of the other immortals. They sit around a table. The most remarkable is Tieguai (Iron Stick) Li, who is said to be the head of the eight immortals. He has an earthly beggar's form with unkempt hair tied up by gold hoop, a dirty face, and a crippled leg. He is in rags and tatters, leans on an iron crutch, and carries a large gourd full of medicine. He should not be belittled, because his iron crutch can change into an immortal dragon when being cast into the air.

Lu Dongbin sits by Tieguai Li. He, known as "Sword Immortal", "Wine Immortal" and "Poet Immortal", has a comely face and elegant manners. Inside his sleeves are hidden a black-snake-shaped short sword and a jade vertical bamboo flute.

The beautiful fairy was called He Xiangu, who was originally a mortal girl in the world of men. She was admired by the Xiwangmu and given several immortal peaches to be eaten, and subsequently became a fairy who could fly in the heavens, live forever and never grow old.

The immortal who sits by He Xiangu has a white nose, wears a cap of red rope and black gauze, and holds court ritual in his hands. He has the look of a clown crossed with a county magistrate. It is said that he was a king's relative before becoming an immortal and was called Cao Guojiu.

An old immortal with white hair and beard, named Zhang Guolao, takes the seat of honor. Inside his bosom is hidden a donkey made of white paper. It is said that if he lightly blows one breath over it, the paper-made donkey will turn into a real donkey which can cover thousands of leagues in a single day.

The immortal nearby Zhang Guolao has a red face, leopard-like eyes, long beard, a belly and two buns coiled in various shapes on the top of his head. He is usually shown waving a palm fan. With an appearance of might he was said to have once been a brave general named Han Zhongli in the Han Dynasty (206 BC-220).

Two young immortals take the right-hand seat, side by side. The one near whom a basket of fresh flowers is placed is called Han Xiangzi. He is said to be the nephew of Han Yu, a great writer of the Tang Dynasty (618-907). The other, who is usually dressed in blue tatters, with one foot bare and the other in a boot and also wearing a three-cun-wide wooden waistband while holding a three-chi-long clapper in his hand, is Lan Caihe.

These eight immortals simply sit around a square table. Later this kind of square table became known as an Eight Immortals Table. Legend has it that the eight drank to their heart's content. After the banquet was over and the eight immortals bad farewell to the Xiwangmu, a while later they came to the skies over the East Sea by flying up to the clouds.

But let us return to the present. The billows roll on and go up to sky, producing howl great enough to shake the universe. Of course it is very easy for the eight immortals, who can speed across the sky in order to cross the sea. The youngest of them, Han Xiangzi, who is both lively and mischievous, suggests all of a sudden, "Various immortal friends, it is so insipid to cross the sea by flying up to the clouds. It would be far better for each of us to drop a treasure onto the surface of the sea, and cross the sea by taking it. How delighted that would be!" The other immortals think this is very funny. On the other hand, having eaten their fill and with a high mood, they all want to show their special skills; so they all agree.

How supernatural Tieguai Li is! As soon as being plunged into the sea, his iron crutch turns into a dragon, prancing away on

the surface of the waves. Tieguai Li jumps down from the cloud and stands on back of the dragon, carrying a bone in his teeth. Han Xiangzi is unwilling to fall behind and throws a basket full of flowers into the sea. The flowers in the basket overspread the surface of the sea and he stands on them, thus bestriding the ocean.

Lu Dongbin casts down his vertical jade flutes. Although the jade falling to the surface of the sea does not cover a large area, it is just sufficient for Lu Dongbin to stand on. The sea breeze blows through the flute, producing a beautiful melody.

"Lan Caihe singing and dancing, and how many Lan Caihe there are in the world?" Accompanied by the music of the flute, a wandering Taoist named Lan Caihe sings for joy while standing at the helm of a big clipper. The clipper cutting through the waves is like a jade raft carrying Lan Caihe ever forward across the ocean.

"How many people there are in the

The Eight Immortals Cross the Sea

world, but no one is like me, an old fellow; not riding a donkey with his face towards the back, but viewing all the things ahead of me!" Zhang Guolao sings while beating the bamboo chips. The paper-made donkey falls down to the surface of the sea. In a very short time, a white donkey floats above the waves and Zhang Guolao rides it, facing backward and driving it towards the opposite shore.

Several other immortals descend from the clouds in quick succession, with Cao Guojiu riding on a jade piece, Han Zhongli on a war drum, and He Xiangu on a bamboo plaque. The eight immortals each ride on their own treasure and brave the wind and the waves, attracting the attention of the dragon king, shrimp soldiers and crab generals who live in the sea. They all cheer, shouting, "Look, the eight immortals cross the sea, each showing his or her special ability."

The Weaving of a Dream

Long ago, there was a thatched cottage at the foot of a mountain, in which there lived an old Zhuang widow who had three sons. The widowed master weaver completed a Zhuang brocade, on which there were houses, gardens, orchards, kaleyards and fish ponds, as well as chickens, ducks, oxen and sheep.

One day, the wind blew it away toward the east of Heaven. It turned out that it was taken away by a group of fairies in the Taiyangshan Mountain who wanted it as a design sample.

The old woman asked her eldest son to go to the east and retrieve it for her. Because he could not bear hardship, he was given a box of gold by an old grandmother and went back to the city to live in ease and comfort. The old woman asked her second son to do the same thing and he, like his elder brother, could not bear hardship, got a box of gold from an old grandmother and went back to the city to enjoy an easy life.

With the help of a big stone horse, the youngest son of the old woman crossed the volcano and the sea, located the fairy in red, and asked her to return the Zhuang brocade. The fairy in red was weaving another brocade with the Zhuang brocade by the old woman as an example. The youngest son took the opportunity to take away the Zhuang brocade of his family and returned to his mother, riding the big stone horse. After the third son returned home, the Zhuang brocade gradually extended in the sun and became a beautiful hometown. The fairy who had embroidered

her figure on the Zhuang brocade was brought to their new home. The fairy married the youngest son and they lived there with the weaver happily ever after.

One day, the other two brothers, who had spent all the gold given to them by the old grandmother and become beggars, came back to the village. They felt too ashamed to visit their relatives and left after a few days with their begging bowls in their hands.

Hundreds of Birds

This is a beautiful legend of the Yao people. Long ago, there lived a hardworking and thrifty old man named Chatoya in a small village. He, very good and honest, neither offended another person nor did an evil deed.

Chatoya was 60 years old, but his wife had never borne a child. They felt so anxious about this that they went to worship the Nuwa, in the hope of her bestowing a child on them. Their sincerity moved Nuwa and one night they had the following dream.

They dreamt of a clinquant peacock

which said, "Ah, I want to be your daughter." And the very next day, the wife of Chatoya discovered she was pregnant.

Later, the child was born, who turned out to be a beautiful girl. The couple named their daughter Acha Mana. She was able to walk at the age of six months, grazed the sheep at the age of three, embroidered at the age of six, did farm work at the age of seven, and had mastered all the skills in the world by the time she reached 16.

Beautiful Acha Mana was able to embroider many flowers, grasses and birds true to life with her deft hands at the age of 17. But she was not self-satisfied with this and applied herself to learning embroidery even more studiously. At the age of 18, she was able to embroider a bird which could spread its wings and fly. She embroidered 365 birds within 365 days. These birds multiplied, making the world more colorful.

Knowing this, Henlho, an amative official, wanted to take Acha Mana as his

concubine. Flocks of sheep, herds of oxen and precious jewels could not move her heart. Flustered and exasperated, Henlho took Acha Mana away by force.

When her unfortunate suffering became known among her neighbors they went to her rescue, knives and swords in hand.Henlho was killed, but Acha Mana fell from the cliff.

That evening, the dead girl turned herself into a golden peacock. From then on, there were hundreds of birds headed by the golden peacock who visited the village each year.

Liang Shanbo and Zhu Yingtai

The legend of Liang Shanbo and Zhu Yingtai, regarded as the Chinese equivalent of Romeo and Juliet, is one of China's four major folk legends.

In the reign of Emperor Yinghe of the Eastern Jin Dynasty(317-420), there was a Zhujia Village in the south of the Shanjuanshan Mountain where lived a wealthy family whose patriarch was called Noble Zhu. According to the rule of the Zhu Family, property could not be inherited by a daughter,

but only by a son. Noble Zhu, however, had no son. In order that his family property could be properly inherited, he had made his daughter disguise herself as a boy from early childhood. Yingtai, talented and good looking, was also intelligent and bookish.

When she was of school age, Noble Zhu sent Yingtai to the nearby Bixian'an, an old-style private school, for study. In the school, there was a classmate named Liang Shanbo, who lived in the Liangjiang Village, about 2.5 km west of the Shanjuanshan Mountain. The two felt like old friends at their very first meeting. Therefore, they gathered some soil as incense and took vows of brotherhood in the pavilion of a thatched bridge, at the back of the Shanjuanshan Mountain.

For three years, Yingtai and Shangbo studied in the same school. During this period, they went together to Qi and Lu area (present-day Shandong Province) to worship Confucius and also travelled to Dongwu

(present-day Jiangsu Province). They shared their food in the daytime and their single bed at night. They were nearly always together, and when they were not communicated by writing and replying in poems. Shanbo was not talented, but he was honest and tolerant. Yingtai slowly fell in love with Shanbo. For the three years, Yingtai had not taken off "his" clothes. Though Shanbo puzzled over that, Yingtai never explained. As a result, Shanbo did not see any traces of female characteristics in Yingtai.

After three years, Liang Shanbo was going to travel to Yuhang (present-day Hangzhou) to further his studies, whereas Zhu Yingtai was denied this opportunity by her father. They were reluctant to part with each other, and exchanged tokens of their eternal friendship. Shanbo presented Yingtai with an ancient Qin (musical instrument), while Yingtai presented a gold-plate folded fan in return, on which she had inscribed the two characters "Bianxian." When Shanbo was going to Hangzhou, Yingtai accompanied him for the first 18 miles to send him off. During the journey, Yingtai hinted to Shanbo that she was a girl and that she had fallen in love with him. Shanbo, honest and tolerant, did not catch onto her hidden meaning and did not even have the slightest suspicion that she was not a boy. Just before parting, she told Shanbo that she would be a matchmaker and arrange a union between Shanbo and her sister. Before the two finally exchanged goodbyes, Yingtai reminded Shanbo to pay a visit to her home on a plighted day so that he could propose a marriage to her "sister" (who was, of course, really herself).

After Yingtai returned home from school, her parents unexpectedly betrothed her to a young man surnamed Ma, in Jingtang, west of the county. One day, in a break from studying, Shanbo paid a visit to Yingtai's home. In the rich and lovely dress of a beautiful woman,

Yingtai went up to meet Shanbo who at once recognised her true gender. When Yingtai told Shanbo that her parents were forcing her to marry Ma Wencai, a rich and spoiled gentleman, Liang Shanbo was heartbroken. Before parting, the lovers vowed that if they could not live together, they would die together.

After bidding farewell to each other in tears, Shanbo's health slowly deteriorated to the point where he became seriously ill and later died. He was buried near the Hu Bridge, in the west of his village. Hearing the news, Yingtai was filled with deep sorrow and determined to die for love. On the day Yingtai was to be married to Ma Wencai, Yingtai insisted on passing by the Hu Bridge, thus offering herself as a sacrifice to Shanbo. When the sedan-chair passed by Shanbo's tomb, Yingtai left the procession to pay her respects to Shanbo. Yingtai cried and ran into the stele. Suddenly, there was a strong wind, which

blew the dust and the stones, making the sky dark. All of a sudden, the earth cracked and without hesitation, Yintai leapt into the chasm that had formed. After the wind stopped, Yingtai and Shanbo's spirits had turned into a pair of beautiful butterflies and emerged from the tomb, flying together among the flowers forever, never to be apart again.

Hua Mulan Joining the Army

In the Northern and Southern Dynasties (420-581), there lived a young and beautiful girl in North China who was extremely skilful in martial arts and shooting. She was none other but Hua Mulan.

One day, while she was grazing the village flocks, she saw several boys riding on horseback, armed with bows and arrows to go hunting. She entered into competition with them and unexpectedly bagged the most game. After she went back home, her mother scolded her for laying aside grazing in favor

of hunting and her father cursed her furiously for not following the rules that girls should obey, but secretly felt surprised at the so many birds and animals that she had successfully hunted.

While Mulan was saying that she was able to shoot an arrow through a willow leaf a hundred yards away with every shot hitting the target, the Lizhang, the head of the neighborhood of 25 families, came into their courtyard. Mulan put an arrow to the bowstring and released it, shooting off the cap of the Lizhang, who was understandably astonished. Mulan's father hastened to apologize to him and punished Mulan by ordering her to weave cloth for three days and not to step out of her door.

Lizhang had come to distribute the official dispatch, which said that because of making war with a neighboring country, the Khan was badly in need of soldiers and officers, with the name of Mulan's father being included in the military roster.

At night, Mulan's father talked over the issue with his wife: He was old and frail, their son was still a small child, and their daughter was ineligible. What should he do? The couple were so depressed that they could only sigh. Mulan heard their talk in the next room and stopped weaving to sigh also.

Mulan did not sleep for a whole night and finally had a good idea. In the early morning of the next day, she sneaked out of her parents' house, went to the market, bought a horse equipped with saddle, bridle and long whip, and had a campaign gown sewn. Then, Mulan had her long hair cut, wrapped her head in a kerchief, put on her military costume, and mounted the date-red horse, being now disguised as a young male soldier.

After getting everything ready, Mulan rode the horse and gallopped back home like the wind. Her parents almost failed to recognize her. She told them the truth. Since what is done cannot be undone and there was no better way, her parents had no option but

花木兰从军

Hua Mulan Joining the Army

to let Mulan join the army. They shed loving tears to bid farewell to Mulan.

Mulan hurried to the border along with the main army. Having marched a long way, the army was now bivouacked by the Yellow River. What greeted the ears of Mulan, now dressed as a soldier, was no longer her parents' call, but the gurgles and splashes of the rushing waters.

After resuming their march, the army arrived at the foot of the Black Hill, which was close to the enemy's camp. What greeted the ears of Mulan, who was preparing for the battle to come, was no longer her parents'call, but the enemy's horses neighing.

On the ensuing expedition, which encompassed thousands of miles to the war, she dashed across mountains and passes as if in flight. In the chilly northern border, her armour and helmet glistened under the frosty moonlight and the drum beat sounding the night watches rang with the coldness of steel against steel.

Going through thousands of battles and experiencing many narrow escapes, Mulan, sharp-witted and brave, was promoted time after time and finally became a general due to her valor and tactical awareness.

After 12 years' war, she returned in triumph. The Emperor granted Mulan a private audience, giving her a reward of much gold and silver and many treasures and promoting her to the position of minister of war.

Mulan joined the army in place of her father for the common people and the country she loved. She neither wanted gold nor silver nor treasures, neither did she want to severe as the minister of war. She asked only for a camel being fleet of foot, which she could ride to return home and take care of their parents.

Some 12 years later, her parents had become grey-haired. When they heard that their daughter was coming, they came to the crossing, each helping the other, to receive her; her younger brother, who had by now

grown up, whetted a knife and slaughtered a pig and a sheep to reward his sister with a suitable banquet.

Mulan finally returned, riding on the camel, accompanied by several comrades-in-arms. Her parents were asked to treat her comrades-in-arms in the hall, while she went to her own room by herself. She took off her military costume, replaced it with the clothes of a beautiful lady, combed her cloud-like hair and adorned her face with lotions and powders, checking herself before the mirror after which she went to greet her guests.

All her comrades-in-arms were astonished to see General Hue who turned out to be a girl.

Shennong Tasting All Kinds of Herbs and Plants

Legend has it that Shennong had a transparent stomach from birth so that the five internal organs and six hollow organs could be clearly seen. In those days, people fell ill and even met with their death because of eating at will. Shennong determined to taste all things. He put those things that were tasty into a bag on the left of his body, which he provided for others, while putting those which he deemed unpalatable into the bag on the right side of his body, as a sort of repository.

神农尝百草

Shennong Tasting All Kinds of Herbs and Plants

One time, Shennong tasted a tender leaf. After the leaf was swallowed and entered the stomach, it just swabbed the various organs around it cleanly, as if it were going on a tour of inspection. Shennong therefore named it "Inspector," although the later generations called it "tea." Shennong put it into the bag on the left.

On a second occasion, Shennong tasted a damask, butterfly-like flower. It was a little sweet, with a delicate fragrance, and was in fact what we call "licorice." He put it into the bag on the right.

Shennong tasted all kinds of plants and herbs. Whenever he found he was poisoned, he saved himself with the tea. There were 47,000 varieties of flowers, herbs, roots and leaves in the bag on the left, and 398,000 in the bag on the right.

One day, however, Shennong ate a sample of intestine-breaking grass. This kind of grass was so poisonous that he died without

having time to counter its effects with the tea. He sacrificed his own life in order to save all others. To commemorate his self-sacrifice, he was honored as "Medicine King Bodhisattva".

Ximen Bao Throwing the Witch Into the River

In the Warring States Period (475 BC-221 BC), Ximen Bao was posted to the city of Yedu (present-day Linzhang County in Henan Province) as an administrative officer. When he took up residency in the city, he was surprised by the low population density of the city and its outskirts. He asked for the reason why there were so few people living there.

An old man with a white beard replied, "It was because Hebo, the god of the Zhanghe River, wanted to marry. Every year he wanted a beautiful bride. If the citizens refused his

demand he would cause the river to swell and inundate their farm lands and houses. ”

Ximen Bao asked, “Who was the one who first started to believe in this?”

The old man said, “according to the local witch they have to oblige. The local district officer and the gentry took the opportunity of the wedding ceremony to force the common people to donate money. Every year they asked them to donate over a million tales of gold but only 20 or 30 percent of this amount was actually spent on the celebration of the river god’s wedding. The rest of the money they divided among themselves.”

“Where was the bride obtained from?” asked Ximen Bao.

The old man answered, “The witch would lead some persons to go to those families who had a young and beautiful daughter. The family of the girl would be frightened into paying a large sum of money to have their girl spared. They would then go around searching for another girl. If the

family of any girl so found could not afford to pay them they would marry her off to the river god. When the auspicious day for the wedding arrived, the girl who was made up would be placed on a mat made of reeds. The girl and the mat would be pushed and allowed to drift off in the running water. After drifting for a while, the mat would sink. Therefore, those families who have a daughter have moved away from this district and gone to live elsewhere. That is why there are not many people living here and why they are so poor."

Ximen Bao asked whether their lands had ever been flooded after Zhanghe River god found a new wife.

The old man replied, "They are still flooded. The witch said that it was very fortunate to send a bride for the river god, otherwise flooded even more."

Ximen Bao said, "The river god shows its presence or power! I ask to be informed when the next wedding is due so that I can see off the new bride."

On the day of the next wedding, there were many people gathered along the riverside. Ximen Bao, as the officer in charge of the city, arrived with a contingent of soldiers. The witch, gentry and district officers hurried to receive him. The witch, aged over 70, was followed by a dozen pretty and coquettish female disciples.

Ximen Bao said, "Bring the bride here and let me see whether she is beautiful." After a little time, the girl was brought out. Ximen Bao saw the girl shedding tears, turned around and said to the witch: "No. The girl is not beautiful enough. Witch, would you please go to the river and inform the river god that another beautiful girl will be found and sent out in a few days." Without any delay the soldiers threw the witch into the river. After waiting for some time Ximen Bao complained, "Why has the witch not come back? Let one of her disciples hasten her." The soldiers grabbed one of her disciples and tossed her into the river; a few time later, he

西门豹治邺

Ximen Bao Throwing the Witch Into the River

ordered that another disciple be thrown. Then, he said, "We have found that these women cannot do what we desire. Gentry and district officers, would you please beg the river god for leniency." He was going to order his soldiers to throw them into the river. These gentry and district officers were so frightened as to kneel down and beg for mercy. Some of them even bowed so low as to break their heads. Ximen Bao said, "Okay. Let us wait for a while." Then, he simply said, "Stand up. It seems that the river god will keep them. You can all go back home. "

The common people took a tumble. It turned out that the witch and the district officer had a dirty trick going and had swindled the money. From then on, no one dared to mention the idea of "having a new bride for the river god."

Ximen Bao mobilized the common people to cut 12 dykes, thus introducing the water of the Zhanghe River onto the land. From then on, bumper harvests were gathered on both banks of the Zhanghe River every year.

The Cowherd and the Weaving Maid

Long, long ago there was an Altair and a Vega in the sky watched by the Qianniu and the Weaving Maid respectively. They hit it off and discovered a mutual affinity. However, boys and girls were not allowed to fall into love without permission in accordance with the laws of heaven. The Weaving Maid was the granddaughter of the Xiwangmu (Queen Mother of the West), who ousted Qianniu into the earthly world and ordered the Weaving Maid to make a colorful brocade as beautiful as the clouds as her punishment.

The Weaving Maid wove layers of beautiful clouds with a kind of supernatural silk on her loom. At different times and seasons, the cloud presented different colors. This is the clothing of heaven. From the time Qianniu was demoted, the Weaving Maid was deeply sad and shed many tears. She ceaselessly wove the beautiful brocade of cloud, hoping that the Xiwangmu would show mercy to Qianniu, thus allowing him to return to heaven. One day, several fairy maids implored the Xiwangmu to allow them to visit the Bilianchi Pond. Being in a good mood, the Xiwangmu gave them her permission. Meanwhile, they found the Weaving Maid terribly depressed, and begged Xiwangmu to let her go with them. The Xiwangmu dearly loved her granddaughter and ordered them to go and return quickly.

After Qianniu was demoted, he was born into the family of a farmer and named Niulang (cowherd). Later his parents died and he had to subsist in hardship with his brother and sister-in-law. In fact they were so harsh to the Cowherd that they gave him only a single cow when dividing up family property.

From then on, the Cowherd and the cow depended on each other for survival. They engaged in farming and built their house on a strip of barren land. They barely kept body and soul together. Apart from the cow (which of course could not speak) there was only the Cowherd in the house, and he was very lonely. The cowherd did not know that this old cow was really Taurus.

One day, the cow suddenly began to speak. It said, "Cowherd, you must go to the Bilian Pond, where the fairies will come to bathe. Take the red clothes you find there, and the one to whom they belong will be your wife." The Cowherd was astonished and happy at the sound of the cow speaking human language. He asked, "Brother Cow, are you really able to speak? And is what you said really true?" The cow nodded his head. Then the Cowherd stealthily hid himself in the reeds near the Biyao Chi and awaited the arrival of the fairies.

Soon the fairies lightly arrived, took off their clothes, and jumped into the pond. The Cowherd immediately dashed out from behind the reeds and took away the red immortal clothes. Seeing people coming, the fairies hasted to put on their own clothes and flew away like birds, with the fairy who had no clothes to wear being left behind. With no clothes the Weaving Maid was shy and anxious, but had no way out. Then, the Cowherd went up to her and asked her to be his wife so that he could give her back her clothes. As soon as she fixed her eyes upon him, she knew that the cowherd was none other than the very Qianniu who she missed every day. She immediately said yes. And so it happened that the Weaving Maid became the Cowherd's wife.

After they were married, the Cowherd engaged in farming while the Weaving Maid wove. They loved each other and lived a

happy life. Before long, they had a son and a daughter. They were content to think that they would live into old age together.

Meanwhile, the Xiwangmu gave vent to her rage and sent immortals and fairies to catch the Weaving Maid so she could receive punishment in heaven.

One day, the weaving maid was cooking, when the Cowherd hasted to return from the field, telling her with his eyes in tears, "Brother Cow is dead. Before his death, it said its hide should be peeled off and put aside. Another day, the one who is wrapped in it will fly up to heaven."

Hearing this news, the Weaving Maid feel puzzled. She knew that the old cow was in fact Taurus. He had himself been demoted just because he had spoken up for Qianniu. Why did he die so suddenly? The Weaving Maid let the Cowherd peel off the hide and they buried the cow with great ceremony.

Then, a strong wind blew and the heavenly soldiers and officers descended

and escorted Weaving Maid up into the sky without offering any explanation.

While flying, Weaving Maid heard the Cowherd shouting, "Weaving Maid, wait for me." Turning her head, she saw the Cowherd wrapped in the cowhide and carrying their son and daughter in wicker baskets. Slowly, the gap between them closed and the Weaving Maid could see the lovely appearance of her son and daughter. The children opened their arms and cried "Mama!"

The Cowherd and the Weaving Maid were almost within touching distance when the Xiwangmu herself appeared above the clouds. She pulled a gold hairpin out of her hair and drove it between them. Suddenly, they were divided by the Milky Way.

Looking helplessly at the cowherd and their children, the Weaving Maid cried out until her voice became hoarse and she had not an ounce of strength left. Her cries and those of her children were loaded with grief and tears. Even the fairies and the immortals were full of tender emotion. Seeing this, the Xiwangmu herself was also moved by the genuine love between the cowherd and the Weaving Maid. She agreed that the Cowherd and their children could stay in heaven and meet with the Weaving Maid on the 7th day of the 7th lunar month.

From then on, the Cowherd lived in heaven and looked at the Weaving Maid across the Milky Way. At night in autumn, among the numerous stars, we can see that there are two bigger stars glittering at either end of the Milky Way, and these are Vega and Altair. On either side of Altair there are also two smaller stars, which are the son and daughter of the Cowherd and the Weaving Maid.

On the 7th of the 7th lunar month, when the Cowherd and Weaving Maid are due to meet, numerous magpies fly up to make a bridge for them. On this bridge of magpies, the Cowherd and the Weaving Maid have their a reunion. They look at each other

and embrace their son and daughter, having many words to say and much affection to tell. Legend has it that if people quietly listen under the grape vine on the 7th day of the 7th lunar month, they will hear the Cowherd and the Weaving Maid talking with immortal music in the background. It is unbearable to meet as well as to depart. They look forward to their reunion on the 7th day of the 7th lunar month each year.

Many writers and poets of the past dynasties wrote poems to eulogize this love story. Of these the most popular is the "Fairy of The Magpie Bridge" by Qin Guan, a poet of the Song Dynasty (960-1279):

Dainty clouds she dexterously weaves; her grief of separation the shooting stars transmit; and in secrecy, across the Milky Way the river vast, they reunite.

Admidst golden winds and silvery frost, their yearly rendezvous proves more affectionate than many a worldly trysting night.

With feelings as tender as water and after a reunion as fleeting as a dream, they can hardly turn and embark on their homeward journey.

After all, when love is genuine and perpetual, it really matters not if a couple are always in each other's sight.

Later, on the 7th day of the 7th lunar month when the Cowherd and the Weaving Maid met, girls would come by the flowers under the moonlight, look up at the sky, and try to spot Vega and Altair on either side of the Milky Way. They hope to see the annual reunion, while at the same time praying that they be quick-witted and nimble-fingered, and have a good marriage. This is the Double Seventh Festival, the most romantic of China's traditional festivals, as well as one that young girls pay special attention to.

Great Wall Collapsed as Meng Jiangnu Cried

This story occurred long, long ago. At that time Emperor Qinshihuang of the Qin Dynasty (221-206 BC) conscripted 800,000 men to build the Great Wall. Local governments all along the projected route rounded up young men to help to complete the gigantic project. Those who were pressganged and sent to the project site toiled around the clock and many of them were worked to death.

In Suzhou there lived a scholar named Fan Qiliang, who hid himself in all kinds

of different places to evade the government troops. One day, he hid himself in the garden of the Meng Family where he happened to meet Meng Jiangnu, who was a beautiful and smart girl. She and her parents hid Fang Qiliang again. Her parents liked him too, and so permitted Meng Jiangnu to marry him. Less than three days after their marriage, Fan Qiliang was caught and transferred to the Great Wall construction site to do hard labor under the command of bailiffs in a feudal yamen. She cried a river, missing him very much and bitterly awaiting his return.

Half a year later, she still had no news from Fan Qiliang. It was late autumn and the northerly were coming and the reed catkins were becoming white and it was colder day by day. Meng Jiangnu thought that because her husband was building the Great Wall in north China, he must be very cold. She sewed some winter clothes for him and set out to go to the Great Wall and find her husband.

On the road, she weathered many

hardships, eventually arriving at the foot of the Great Wall. Unexpectedly, a worker told her that Fan Qiliang had died and that his corpse had been buried under the Great Wall. After hearing this heartrending piece of news, Meng Jiangnu felt that there was nothing but gloom above and darkness below, and fainted with sorrow and exhaustion. After regaining consciousness, she burst into floods of bitter tears. She cried so desperately that the heavens were moved by her tears and the sun and moon put out their lights.

Suddenly a trumpet blast rocked the sky and the earth and a part of the Great Wall stretching dozens of kilometers collapsed, exposing thousands of skeletons of those who had died in its construction. Meng Jiangnu bit her finger, and dropped some blood on every skeleton. She prayed secretly that if it was her husband's skeleton, the blood would infiltrate into it, while if not it would flow in four directions. Finally Meng Jiangnu found the skeleton of her husband. She held the bones in

孟姜女哭长城

Great Wall Collapsed as Meng Jiangnu Cried

her arms, weeping bitterly.

Thinking Meng Jiangnu very beautiful, Emperor Qinshihuang wanted to force her to be his concubine. Meng Jiangnu pretended to agree, but asked the emperor to complete three tasks first: Monks were invited to recite scriptures for Fan Qiliang for 49 days and rebury his skeleton gracefully; Emperor Qinshihuang personally led all his ministers to offer sacrifice to Fan Qiliang; after Fan Qiliang was buried, Meng Jiangnu visited scenes at different spots for three days before marrying Emperor Qinshihuang. The emperor agreed to her requirements. After the three things were done, Meng Jiangnu severely scolded the emperor and committed suicide by jumping into the sea.

The Old Man under the Moon

During the time of the Tang Dynasty (618-907), there was a man called Wei Gu. One day he traveled to the town of Song.

When he was strolling aimlessly around the streets at night, he saw an old man sitting by the road, with a big bag by his side. The old man was reading a big thick book. Wei Gu was very curious, and so he asked him "Old man, what book are you reading?"

"It is the World Book of Marriage for men and women." replied by the old man.

"How strange" said Wei Gu. "A World

Book of Marriage for men and women. I have read many books but have never heard of this one. May I ask what's in your bag?" Wei Gu was, as we have said, a very curious man.

"The bag is filled with magic red ropes. Even if two people are the bitterest of enemies; even if they live many leagues apart in different countries, if I tie this red rope on their feet, they will end up as a couple madly in love with each other."

"Really? So, you maybe know who will be my future wife?" asked Wei Gu with great interest.

"Of course I know. Let me have a look....Ah here it is! Your future wife is the daughter of the woman selling vegetables in the north end of the market."

Wei Gu was surprised, "You mean my wife will be the daughter of a family who sell vegetables?"

"Yes. I can take you to have a look if you like. You see, there is a little girl behind the stall there. She will be your wife. Can you see

her?"

"What? You mean her. How old is she?"

"She is two years old."

"So little, how can she be my wife?"

"Hey, look my friend it doesn't matter what age she is now. She will grow up."

"When will we get married?"

"What's the hurry?"

"The girl is poor and ugly. Why did you arrange such a bad marriage for me?"

"Don't be like that my friend. You will definitely appreciate me in the future. Mark my words." No sooner had the old man finished these words when he disappeared into thin air.

After getting home, Wei Gu was very unhappy. He thought "I'm the son of a rich family. How can I marry such a poor and ugly girl? To avoid this terrible fate I must end that girl's life before she grows up."

He thought it over again and again but could see no alternatives. He called his servant named A Fu.

"Yes, master."

"You go to the food market. There is a stall selling vegetables in the north of the market. It is run by a woman with the surname Chen. She has a two-year-old daughter. I want you to kill the girl for me."

"Why?"

"Someone told me my fortune that seemingly she will be my future wife. You see my problem? How could such a lowly girl ever be a match for me?"

"Master, how can I kill a two-year-old child? It's impossible…."

"You must do, A Fu. Do you really want your master to be so shamed? Don't worry. I will reward you well.."

A Fu reluctantly agreed.

The servant went to the market and found the vegetable stall and saw the little girl. He struck at her with his knife but because he was so nervous, he only hit the girl a glancing blow on her forehead. The market was crowded, so he dared not try to finish the

job. He escaped at once and never returned to Wei Gu or to that town.

Fourteen years later, Wang Qin, Inspector of Xiangzhou, married his daughter to Wei Gu. The girl was about 16 years old and was a most beautiful and elegant maiden. She was fair of complexion apart from a scar on her forehead. Wei Gu's curiosity had never left him and he couldn't help himself asking his new bride one day, "How did you get that scar on your forehead?"

"I'm the adopted daughter of the inspector. Fourteen years ago, my mother took me to sell vegetables on the market in the town of Song. One day, a bandit tried to kill me in the market. Luckily he just hit me in the forehead with his knife and I survived. That is how I got the scar."

"The food market of the town of Song?" said Wei Gu in horror. "Are you referring to the food market of the town of Song?"

"Yes, why?"

"It was me. I sent that man to kill you. I

am damned, I am damned!"

"You? Why did you do it?"

Wei Gu hung his head in shame and did his best to explain the events of fourteen years ago. To his astonishment, his wife was very understanding. "Don't be sorry. Dry your eyes my husband. It is all in the past. I forgive you but we need to stand together now. We must be in good harmony for when we one day meet again that old man."

The couple lived happily and never forgot that old man under the moon with a book and a magic rope.

Lord Bao Interrogates a Stone

Once upon a time, there was a poor child living in a small town. His father had died and his mother was very sick. Every day, he got up before dawn, carried a basket of twisted dough sticks which he would deep-fry and sell to people in the market. His voice would ring out bravely, "Deep-fried dough sticks. Only two coppers."

One day, he sold all his dough sticks. He sat on a piece of stone, and counted out all the copper coins from his basket. There were 100!

"What a good day's work!", the boy thought. Because he had been frying the dough sticks all day, his hands were coated with grease. As he counted up his copper coins, the copper coins too became coated with grease. Looking at these greasy and flashing copper coins, the little boy was very happy. He was pretty sure that today's income - 100 copper coins - would enable him to buy some good medicine for his mother. The little boy had worked so hard all morning that as he leaned against a nearby stone he soon fell sound asleep. When he woke up, he immediately wanted to go and get the medicine for his mother. As he rose to his feet, however, he realized to his horror that all the copper coins in the basket had been stolen. The little boy was heartbroken and wept bitterly at the injustice of life.

Just then, Lord Bao was passing through the market. Lord Bao was a jurist of some renown. He had a black face and a blacker beard, and was known far and wide as "Black

Lord Bao." He was extremely wise and his brilliance as a jurist had helped to settle many legal disputes. He saw the child weeping and gently asked him, "Child, why do you cry?" The boy explained how his money had been stolen. "Who stole your money?" asked Lord Bao. "I don't know." replied the boy. "I was just leaning against this piece of stone when I must have fallen asleep. When I woke, I found my money was gone. I can't get the medicine for my sick mother." The child resumed his heartrending cries.

Lord Bao looked around and was lost in thought for a moment. Eventually he said in a loud voice, "I know what happened. It was this piece of stone that stole your money." Thinking he was making sport of the boy, a few people began to gather round. "Let me interrogate this piece of stone for you and ask it to return the money to you."

The people were delighted with this fun and collapsed in laughters, "How could a

Lord Bao Interrogates a Stone

stone steal money?" "How can you interrogate a stone?" "I heard this Lord Bao was a wise man, but he seems like an awful langer to me."

Lord Bao pretended to be very angry. He shouted theatrically, "I am trying to interrogate this stone. How can you ignorant people laugh at a wise counsel like me? Each of you is fined a copper coin for insolence." The people thought this was hilarious and eagerly lined up to "pay" their fine. Lord Bao ordered his servant to borrow a basin and he poured some water into it.

The people queued up throw their copper into the basin. Thump, thump, thump....They threw in their coins laughing all the time. A man came up and threw in his copper. Immediately Lord Bao ordered his servant to grab the man. Lord Bao pointed at this man and said, "This is the man who stole the boy's copper coins."

Lord Bao had noticed that the copper

coin thrown into the basin had caused a layer of oil to form on the surface of the water. All of the stolen copper coin would have been covered in oil and so the man must have been the thief.

The thief was publicly shamed and had no choice but to return the 100 copper coins to the child. Everyone applauded and marvelled at the wisdom and intelligence of Lord Bao.

The Horse-head Fiddle

Once upon a time, there lived on the Mongolian Chahar Grassland a shepherd boy named Su He. One day, he discovered a little white foal which had become separated from its mother. Su He took care of the white foal, looking after it with great care. Soon it grew into a fine horse with snow-white hair. The horse was very healthy and strong and could run like the wind. The horse helped Su He protect his sheep and drive away wolves. The white horse and Su He were inseparable and became better friends than any humans could be.

In spring one year, the prince of the kingdom announced that he was holding a great horse race. He promised a flock of sheep and his daughter's hand to the winner of the race.

Su He and his fine white horse entered the race. They galloped off like lightning leaving the other horses behind and won the race easily.

The prince was very upset. How could he marry his daughter to a lowly shepherd boy? That was out of the question. In addition the prince cast covetous eyes on the fine white horse and resolved to have it for himself.

The prince offered Su He 3 golden horseshoes in return for his horse. This was more gold than Su He had ever seen in his life but nevertheless he rejected the offer immediately. "I will never sell my horse", he declared.

The prince was determined however and he ordered his servants to attack Su He

and as the young shepherd lay stunned on the ground, they grabbed his white horse.

Su He was rescued by the other herders. When he had recovered from his wounds, he was broken-hearted. He missed his best friend - the white horse so much. One evening, he had just gone to bed when he heard a noise outside his door. He ran out and found his white horse lying on the ground before the door with seven or eight arrows stuck in his body. The shepherd boy wept uncontrollably as the little white horse died in his arms.

What had happened was after the prince had stolen the white horse, he wanted to ride it around court to show off. However whenever he tried to mount the horse, it bucked violently and tried to throw him off. After a couple of attempts the horse broke loose and galloped away. The prince ordered his servants to shoot at the white horse and using their bows they hit the horse with a number of poisonous arrows. The little white horse used the last of its ebbing strength to return to the

Mongolian tent of its only friend Su He and it was there that it died..

After the death of the little white horse, Su He was so sad that he could hardly eat or sleep. One evening, he dreamed that his little white horse had returned to life. It had run up to him from where the sun rises and said to him in a soft voice, "Little master, I'm back and will never leave you. You must use my veins and bones to make a fiddle so that I can be with you forever. "

As soon as he awoke, Su He set to work carving the bones of the white horse into a horse-head shape. He fashioned a neck and made the veins into strings, and the tail into a bow. This was the first horse-head fiddle, and it became the most famous Mongolian traditional instrument.

From then on, the wonderful sound of the horse-head fiddle spread everywhere on the grassland. As long as they could hear those sweet notes from the horse-head fiddle accompanied by a harmonious singing voice

the people would smile and laugh and forget the hardships of their life.

The Mongolian people have another legend about the origin of their beloved horse-head fiddle. This story goes that during the horse-racing at the Nadam Fair - the biggest festival of the year - a poor young hero, Su He, won the race on his white horse. A great duke of the kingdom was enraged at being beaten by such a lowly commoner and with great cruelty he shot the horse dead. Su He was heartbroken and wept bitter tears. That night he met his horse in a dream. In the dream, the horse told Su He to fashion a fiddle from wood with the head of the fiddle carved in the shape of a horse's head and to use the hair of a horse's tail for the strings. The lad did as he was told and the fiddle he made produced extremely sonorous music. From then on, people loved this instrument and composed many songs to accompany this beguiling music.

Heshouwu, the Buckwheat Tuber

Once upon a time, there lived a mother and her son named He at the foot of Mount Yunu in the Songshan Mountains. The son who was named Shouhu was extremely intelligent and from the time he learned to read was always a great scholar.

He passed the county level imperial examination at the age of 19 and became a Xiucai. The other villagers were very happy and they implored him, "Shouhu, work hard and you may pass the provincial level imperial exams ." Shouhu agreed and he redoubled his efforts at his studies. The other villagers helped him and his mother out bringing food and clothes for them, and some even helping them to farm their land. They hoped that Shouhu would gain success in the imperial exams and bring great honor to their village.

Inspired by their encouragement, Shouhu did not leave his house for 300 days. After the Spring Festival, he went to the provincial capital to participate in the imperial exams . When the results were announced, amazingly, Shouhu, a simple mountain peasant, had won the first place – an honored position known as Xieyuan.

At that time the local provincial magistrate was planning to select a husband for his daughter. On the day when the results of the provincial imperial examination were posted, he asked an intermediary to approach Shouhu about marrying his daughter. The family and neighbors of Shouhu were very happy. For them it was a double happiness after Shouhu's success in the exams.

Several days later, the magistrate threw a banquet to celebrate the impending marriage.

When he first caught sight of He Shouhu, the magistrate was very disappointed. Shouhu had many wrinkles on his face and was as thin as a rake. He looked over 40 years old. The magistrate felt that such a person was not an appropriate son-in-law. But what was done was done he thought to himself. He would have to put up with it. At least, he comforted himself Shouhu was a successful candidate in the provincial imperial examinations.

At the banquet, all the guests including the prefecture leader and county officials proposed a toast to the bridegroom. He Shouhu was a poor peasant. He had never seen such a scene and was unsure how he should respond. After drinking several cups of wine, he began to sweat and so took off his hat, revealing a head of grey almost white hair. The guests began to mutter to one another saying, "Look, the son-in-law of the magistrate is an old man?" The magistrate

couldn't take it any more. He thought that Shouhu had cheated him. He flew into a rage and shouted in front of everyone, "This old man has concealed his age. Drive him out of my mansion." Shouhu was unceremoniously thrown out of his own betrothal banquet.

He had been such a diligent scholar and had focused so much on his studies that he had neglected to take care of his body. He hardly washed and never looked in the mirror. Now he borrowed a copper mirror and was horrified at his white-headed and very thin appearance. He was greatly shocked and saddened. What was the point of the scholarly life he thought if this is what it brings you. Surely it would be better to be a farmer.

The following day, Shouhu laid down his pen and his reading glasses and picked up a hoe and went to the Songshan Mountain to start working on the land.

He began his work at the back of Mount Qingtong and worked like a man possessed..

One day, he felt very hungry, thirsty and

tired. Nearby, he saw a plant growing with great profusion in the grass. The plant had heart-shaped leaves and green white flowers. Using his hoe, he dug at the plant's root, finding a small tuber. He picked it up, washed away the dirt, and peeled off the brown skin. The inside was light red brown with a cloud-shaped grain. He took a bite, and it tasted sweet but the end was quite bitter. He ate it all and immediately felt very sated and comfortable.

From that time on, whenever he felt hungry or thirsty, he would dig out some of these tubers and eat them. After a long time, he could feel himself becoming stouter and stronger. He ate the tubers raw or sometimes cooked them in a pot. He spent over 100 days in the mountains.

In autumn when he had harvested his crop Shouhu went down the mountain with his harvest.

When he arrived home, his mother almost didn't recognize him. He had become

Folk Tales

stout and looked much younger and there wasn't a wrinkle on his face. Even more strangely, his white hair had turned black again.

He Shouhu looked into the mirror and found that he looked once again like a young man with a most dignified appearance.

His relatives and friends who visited them saw the new He Shouhu and thought that he must have got the help from the gods. They said to him, "Shouhu, you have been a great scholar. You should not give up. If you go to the capital to participate in the examinations, you could be the country's Number One Scholar (a title conferred on the one who came first in the highest imperial examinations)."

Shouhu readily accepted their advice and once more he returned with a new enthusiasm to his studies. In early spring of the following year, he went to the capital and took part in the final imperial examinations at the Taihe Hall. Amazingly, he won the Tanhua (the third highest score in the imperial

examinations).

At that time the magistrate who had rejected him as his son-in-law the year before had been promoted to the position of Yushi (a high rank). Seeing the Number Three Scholar with his delicate features and black hair, he thought what an impressive handsome man he was. Looking at him carefully, he saw the resemblance to He Shouhu who he had driven out of his house the year before. He questioned him closely. He Shouhu had no hard feelings about what had happened before. He told the magistrate of his adventures as a farmer on the mountain and of how he had discovered this most nutritious of tubers. At the banquet, the guests all applauded He Shouhu for his fortitude and ingenuity.

From then on, all youngsters who found themselves going prematurely grey would go to the Songshan Mountain, to dig up this wonderful tuber and eat it.

This medicinal plant originally had no name. It was discovered by He Shouhu,

and thus was named "He Shouhu." Later, He Shouhu was appointed by the court to be official specialized in providing with suggestions. Thus his name could no longer be used and so the magically medicinal plant was renamed "He Shouwu."

The Legend of the Sworn Brotherhood of the Three Heroes in the Peach Garden

In downtown Zhuoxian County there was a street called Zhongyimiao Street. It is said that the great hero Zhang Fei once sold meat on this street when he lived in Zhuozhou. He used to keep the meat in a well in front of his house which he covered with a heavy flagstone weighing over 500 kg. He also erected a sign by the well with the challenge "Anyone who can lift this stone can have free meat."

One day, Guan Yu was driving his little donkey down that street with a load of mung beans which he hoped to sell. When he got to the doorway of Zhang Fei's butcher's shop, he saw the sign and thought "Hmm - what a rash promise that is!" Guan Yu was very strong and he lifted up the flagstone with very little effort. Laying it to one side he took out a large piece of pork from the well and stored it away on the back of his donkey, Guan Yu continued on his way without saying something. When Zhang Fei returned, his wife told him everything that had happened. Zhang was enraged and immediately went to the market to confront Guan Yu.

Zhang Fei was an impetuous man, but he was no fool. He realized that he needed to settle this problem quietly, or he would have to provide free meat again and again. He came up to Guan Yu, and asked,

"Are your mung beans dry?"

Guan Yu said, "Of course! They are very dry."

"May I check?" inquired Zhang Fei.

"Sure. Go ahead!"

Zhang Fei grasped a handful of mung beans and ground them into powder with his thumb. He did the same with another handful and still he continued. Soon, he had ground half the bag of mung beans into powder. Guan Yu knew that this was the famous Zhang Fei and he beseeched him, "My fellow-villager, if you want to buy my mung beans, please wait to grind them into powder at home after you have bought them. How can I sell them now after you have ground them into powder?"

"Didn't you say I could test them?" Zhang Fei shouted angrily.

"I never said you could test all of them?" replied Guan Yu, also getting angry.

They began to quarrel and soon they had rolled up their sleeves and began trading heavy punches and kicks. People tried to pull apart them but to no avail. At that time, Liu Bei was in the market trying to sell some straw sandals. He saw the fight and seeing that nobody dared to step between the two big fellows, he resolved to make peace between them. Other bystanders told him to stay out of it. He was so slender and slight that they felt he could get seriously hurt if he intervened in the fight between these two huge giants. However, Liu Bei was undeterred. He stepped forward and pulled the two fighters apart easily. Guan Yu and Zhang Fei couldn't touch each other, and they stamped their feet in anger keen to continue beating the heads off each other. This is the origin of the popular saying, "One dragons pulls apart two tigers."

Having fought each other, both Zhang Fei and Guan Yu could not but admire the other's strength. Thanks to Liu Bei's peacemaking, they eventually calmed down and eventually even became good friends. This is how it came to pass that these three great heroes swore a solemn oath of brotherhood in a nearby Peach Garden. Afterwards, they needed to decide the order of seniority. Generally, with sworn blood-brothers rank would be decided according to age. However, Zhang Fei, the youngest among them, wouldn't accept this.

He proposed "We should be ranked according to our strength. The one whose strength is greatest should be regarded as the eldest brother." Guan Yu said, "Liu Bei pulled us two apart with one stroke, so his strength is the greatest and he should be the eldest brother. We are equal, Zhang Fei. There is no need to decide who will be second or third brother. There is no need to fight again."

Zhang Fei remained silent. Then Liu Bei proposed, "Perhaps we can decide this issue with a battle of wits!"

Both Zhang Fei and Guan Yu agreed.

Liu Bei said, "We will see who can throw a chicken feather onto the roof of the house. The one who throws it onto the roof will be the eldest son, OK?"

All three agreed. Short-tempered Zhang Fei caught a chicken and pulled a feather from it and then summoning all his strength he threw it towards the roof. However the feather floated away and even after a number of attempts Zhang Fei was unsuccessful. Guan

Yu also tried and also failed. Then it was Liu Bei's turn. He took the chicken and threw the whole bird onto the roof with no effort at all.

Zhang Fei said, "That doesn't count. You threw the whole chicken!"

Liu answered, "Can you see the chicken feathers on the roof? Who threw them there? I did!"

Zhang Fei was dumbstruck but had to admit that Liu Bei was right. He admitted defeat.

Thus the great hero Liu Bei became the eldest brother, but the question remained of who would be second and third brother? Liu Bei said, "Zhang Fei threw the feather first and the most times, but failed. I believe it is reasonable to rank him as third brother and Guan Yu as second."

Zhang Fei agreed and laughing said, "OK. OK! I give up, I give up!'

This is the first story in the great classic of Chinese literature *The Romance of the Three Kingdoms*. Today, if you mention Liu

Bei, Guan Yu and Zhang Fei to any Chinese people, they will immediately be reminded of the Peach Garden Oath. In the Peach Garden where the peach flowers were in full blossom, the three heroes performed all the sacred rites - prepared a cow and a white horse and burning incense to worship heaven and earth. Then, they established their sworn brotherhood and vowed to fight together and defend each other what may come in those troubled times. If they could not always stand together, they vowed to all die on the same day. The story has been passed down from generation to generation.

The Stories of Avanti

Avanti is a typical character in the legends of the Uygur Ethnic Group. "Avanti" is a generic term which refers to a teacher or scholar and can also be an honorific title. This particular Avanti's name is Nasreddin. To show respect to him, people also call him Hodja · Nasreddin · Avanti (Hodja is also a title, meaning teacher).

In the eyes of the ordinary people, Avanti is the embodiment of wisdom and courage. Even his name is sufficiently magic to make the most woebegone person break out into

laughters.

The classical image of Avanti is one in which he wears a colored ethnic cap and rides on a little donkey facing backwards and this image was established in early times. In China, Avanti is one of the most excellent folk creations.

I Kicked It First

Little Avanti and the other kids felt bored and couldn't decide what to play. A relatively older child said to Avanti, "If you put your cap on the ground and personally kick it, I will make you the king of all the children."

"Isn't it impossible? You see!" Avanti said. Then, he took off his cap, put it on the ground and kicked it. Afterwards, the other kids swarmed around the cap and began to kick it as though it were a ball.

In the evening, seeing the cap was so

dirty, his mother interrogated him, "How did you make this nice cap so dirty?"

"The other kids kicked my cap as though it were a ball." Avanti answered.

"Did you just stand still and look at them kicking your cap instead of stopping them?" his mother replied angrily

"Oh no, Mom. I kicked it first," Avanti said.

I Throw the Cat into It

A mouse fell into a tank full of water in Avanti's house. The little Avanti shouted to his father, "Dad, a mouse has fallen into our water tank!"

"Good grief, hurry up and fish it out!" his father shouted back.

"No need for that, dad, I have thrown our cat into the tank!" the little Avanti answered.

我把猫扔里面了

I Throw the Cat into It

Half of the Reward

Avanti brought some good news to the king, but he took a lot of trouble in doing so.

The king was very pleased after hearing the news and asked Avanti, "What kind of reward do you want for bringing me this news?"

"I would like to suffer fifty lashes." Avanti said.

The king remained perplexed despite much thought and finally ordered that Avanti be given the fifty lashes as requested. At the 25th lash, Avanti shouted, "Stop. Please give the remaining 25 lashes to my colleague!"

"Who is your colleague?" the king asked.

"When I came to call on you, your guard wouldn't allow me to come in. Only after he let me swear to deal out half of my reward to him did he open the door to me."

一半报酬

Half of the Reward

The Day Absent in the World

When Avanti was a dyer, a self-claimed wise man found him with a piece of white hand-woven cloth, saying, "Avanti, please dye this piece of cloth into a kind of color that can't be found anywhere in the world."

"What kind of color do you mean?" Avanti asked.

"It is neither red, nor black, nor blue, nor yellow, nor green nor purple. Anyway, it can't be found in the world." Was the reply.

"All right, I will do as you wish!" Avanti said.

"When should I come to fetch it?" the person asked.

Please come to fetch it on the day absent in the world. It is neither Monday, Tuesday, Wednesday, Thursday, Friday, Saturday nor Sunday." Avanti replied.

Blank Letter

A rich man in the village held a wedding ceremony but he didn't invite Avanti to join. Not thinking much, Avanti folded a piece of blank paper into a square and placed it in an envelope. Carrying the letter, he went to the house of the rich man.

Avanti called the host of the wedding ceremony out and said to him, "Kaze (the Islamic judge) asked me to bring a letter to you." The host was very pleased to hear it and led Avanti to the wedding banquet where Avanti began to taste various kinds of delicacies.

The host opened the envelope and took out the letter to read it. He turned the letter inside out but found no word. He said, "Avanti, what's the matter? There are no words on the letter."

"Perhaps the judge was too busy to write anything." Avanti answered.

空白信

Blank Letter

Let the Aware People Tell the Unaware

One day, Avanti went to a school of philosophy to give a lecture. Stepping onto the platform, he asked the mullas and their disciples, "Do you know what will I lecture to you about?"

"No," everyone replied with one voice.

"It is not interesting to talk with the unaware people," said Avanti. Then, he stepped down from the platform and left.

Several days later, Avanti went there again and repeated the question. This time, everyone answered with one voice, "Yes!"

"It is also not interesting to repeat what you know." said Avanti. Then, he left. For the third time, he put forward the same question. The prepared mullas and their disciples answered, "One half of us know and the other half of us don't!"

"In that way, I ask those who are aware to tell the unaware." Avanti said. Then, he once again stepped down from the platform.

Die Two Days Earlier Than the King

Avanti made a joke with the majordomo of the king. "You will die in two days,." He said. And the next day, the majordomo fell off his horse and was killed.

After the king learned of this, he summoned Avanti to the royal palace, saying, "Avanti, my majordomo died due to you. Are you pleading guilty?"

"Yes, your Majesty," Avanti answered.

"Since you knew when my majordomo would die, do you know the date of your own death?" the king asked.

Avanti shortly understood the meaning of the king and said, "Last night, I saw my

comet. I estimate I will die two days earlier than you."

After hearing that, the king gave up the idea of punishing Avanti at once and secretly blessed Avanti a long life.

Speak a Little Slowly

When Avanti was a disciple, his tutor drummed in that, "My disciples, to really comprehend the essence of every section of the lesson, when you recite it, you should patiently read every sentence one syllable at a time. Moreover, the voice should rise, fall and pause in accordance with the criterion of the lesson."

Avanti had spoken especially fast and fluently from childhood. When he was a student of the school of philosophy, he had answered every question rapidly and exactly. The mulla, somewhat slow in thinking, often couldn't catch what he said.

One day, Avanti answered the question of the mulla quickly. Mulla said to him, "Avanti, you must answer the question more slowly and speak clearly!"

Avanti bore what mulla said in mind. One night, he went to the house of the mulla to consult him about several questions. Mulla asked him to get down the oil lamp on the wall. When he took the lamp, he was a little clumsy and set fire to the mulla's cap that was hanging on the wall.

Avanti said, "Mr....Mull...a...your... cap...has...caught...fire!" By the time he had finished speaking, the cap of the mulla was a pile of ashes.

You Can Grow Wheat Now

At the height of the busy season, Avanti was put into jail. His wife sent him a message saying "Avanti, when do you come back? It is time to grow wheat. I can't plough so much

现在可以种麦子了

You Can Grow Wheat Now

farmland alone."

Avanti wrote back, "My dear wife, you needn't plough the farmland. I have hidden a pot of gold coins in the fields and it is enough for our food and clothes!"

The letters of the criminals must be looked over by the turnkeys. They were extremely pleased to see this letter.

Several days later, Avanti's wife sent a letter again. It said, "Avanti, a large group of people came to turn our ten mu (one fifteenth of one hectare) farmland over two days ago."

Avanti immediately wrote back to his wife after seeing the letter, "It is good. Now you can grow wheat!"

Blow the Trumpet After You Go to Bed

Little Avanti also wanted to blow a trumpet when he saw the other children doing it. He ran up to his father and said, "Papa,

等您睡觉以后再吹

Blow the Trumpet After You Go to Bed

Papa, the other children are blowing their trumpets; please buy a trumpet for me!"

"No, I won't," his father replied. "You make too much noise already. You might make me deaf if you blow a trumpet!"

"Papa, I swear that I will only blow the trumpet after you go to bed if you buy one for me," little Avanti answered.

The Hole Would Be Left

When Avanti was a pupil, the teacher asked him one day, "Avanti, what is four minus four?" Avanti was tongue-tied. The teacher got angry and said "What have you learned in school since you don't even know this. You see, if I put four coins in your pocket, but there is a hole in your pocket and all of them leak out, now what is left in your pocket?"

"The hole," replied Avanti.

Others Can't Do It

Avanti's study was bad at school and his writing was illegible.

One day, the teacher asked him, "Avanti, can you do something that others can't?"

Avanti answered, "Of course I can. For example, I can know what I wrote, but others can't."

Be Able to Calculate on One's Fingers

Avanti sat by a river. Someone asked him, "Avanti, everyone says you are able to calculate on your fingers. In that case, can you tell me if we measure the volume of the water in the river with buckets, how many buckets the water of the river will fill?"

"Let me tell you in this way. If the river

is as big as the bucket, the river can only fill one bucket; and if the bucket is half the size of the river, the river can fill two buckets." answered Avanti.

Modest Sage

One day, Avanti said to the local people, "Allah has given me instruction. From now on, I will become a sage. If you don't believe me, please see my invincible might."

"All right, let us have a look," one of his listeners said. "Could you please move that tree in front of you?"

Avanti silently recited several sections of scripture and blew a deep breath, but the tree remained still. Avanti promptly walked up to the tree, saying, "I'm the most modest of sages. If the tree doesn't want to come to me, I will be happy to go up to the tree."

Black Beards and White Beards

One day, a rich man went to Avanti's barber shop. He wanted to embarrass Avanti, saying, "Avanti, please pick out the white hairs of my beard and shave them!"

"All right, please sit down!" Avanti said. Then, he shaved all the beard of the man and handed the hair to him, saying, "My lord, I'm very busy. You can take the pains to pick out the white hairs from the black ones!"